PRELUDE
TO SURRENDER

PRELUDE TO SURRENDER

THE PAMPLIN FAMILY AND THE SIEGE OF PETERSBURG

Excerpted from
*Heritage: The Making of an
American Family*

by Dr. Robert Pamplin, Jr.

with Gary K. Eisler,
Jeff Sengstack, John Domini

CHESTERFIELD COUNTY PUBLIC LIBRARY
CHESTERFIELD, VA

THE HERITAGE IMPRINT
MASTERMEDIA LIMITED
NEW YORK

In *Prelude to Surrender: The Pamplin Family and the Siege of Petersburg* we have tried to record faithfully, and nowhere to create, a family's history. Reconstruction of events long past entails some speculation. Writing of conversations that no one recorded, we have given the characters words that they might well have spoken.

As we reach the recent past where living memory serves, we have tried to be faithful to the facts as we reliably know them to be. Any inaccuracies are inadvertent; any trespass on the character of any person, living or dead, is absolutely unintended.

DR. ROBERT B PAMPLIN, JR.

Copyright © 1995 by R. B. Pamplin Corporation
and Robert B. Pamplin, Jr.

All Rights reserved, including the right of
reproduction in whole or in part in any form.
Published by MasterMedia Limited.

MASTERMEDIA and colophon are registered trademarks
of MasterMedia Limited

Designed by Michael Woyton
Manufactured in the United States of America
10 9 8 7 6 5 4 3 2 1

CONTENTS

FOREWORD VII

INTRODUCTION IX

THE PAMPLIN FAMILY AND
THE SIEGE OF PETERSBURG 1

PAMPLIN PARK CIVIL WAR SITE 41

PETERSBURG AND THE
OVERALL CAMPAIGN 46

FOREWORD

By Dr. Norman Vincent Peale

A THOUSAND YEARS is an unimaginably long time. We can almost picture our own lives within the span of a century. But no one has a lifespan of a millennium—no individual person can visualize the beginning of a thousand years from the end.

That is what is so fascinating about this book, coming as it does near the end of the Second Millennium: that it tells the story of the past thousand years through many individual generations of one family, who are "climbing the centuries."

The roots of the Pamplin family extend back to Viking Scandinavia, to France and Spain and England, then back to America, the Old South and the Pacific Northwest. The family is older than the countries where they have lived, than the languages they have spoken, than the religious denominations to which they have belonged, than the economic or political systems under which they have lived.

Those of you who have read my book, *The Power of Positive Thinking*, may recall that I was reluctant to complete its writing. There were so many stories yet to be told of all the wonderful things that had been done for people through the "Higher Power"—that is also called God.

There are so many wonderful stories to tell, God has done so much good in this world, that I wished I could have simply kept going with *The Power of Positive Thinking*. And that is another appeal of *Heritage*.

Here is a single family line receiving help from the Higher Power, generation by generation, with challenges most of us have

VII

never dreamed of facing, and overcoming, through positive attitudes. This book tells of family members whose lives are affected by some of the greatest events of the past thousand years.

Heritage...is like *Roots* for its dramatized investigation of ancestors' lives across many generations. As with *Roots*, the authors have started with documented facts about the family members and about the times in which they lived. Using as many authentic quotes as possible from historic figures known to have been acquainted with family members, as well as known circumstances about their lives, the writers then reconstructed and dramatized their life stories.

There may be few other books to offer the remarkable insight *Heritage* does into the English roots of the American Civil War.

This book goes even further, showing how the South's humiliating defeat led to this family's determination to succeed....There may be few books other than *Gone With The Wind* to present the Southern view so eloquently—or so convincingly. And there are probably few others that tell so well what makes the South the South, from the heritage of Slavery to the tobacco and cotton economy.

INTRODUCTION

By Noah Andre Trudeau

THE SPECIAL VALUE of the family saga portrayed in Robert B. Pamplin's *Prelude to Surrender: The Pamplin Family and the Seige of Petersburg* lies not only in its engrossing tale of the remarkable Boisseau clan, but also in the insights shared when individual tales intersect with larger events. For my area of speciality, the Boisseau family history sheds wonderful new light on the Southern home front of that period and much more, because the Boisseaus were fated, through time and geography, to be also on the front line during one of the most intensely waged and surprisingly little known military operations of the Civil War — the ten-month siege of Petersburg, Virginia.

The civilian side of the War Between the States remains a sadly underappreciated side of the conflict. Many of the published diaries and memoirs of the era come from the pens of those who resided near seats of power, and are useful more for understanding political and military happenings than they are for illuminating the day-to-day tribulations of families trying to hold together amidst uncertain times. And of all the civilian experiences of the Civil War, those taking place 1864 and 1865 in Petersburg have especial significance. No other civilian population was under such a direct threat for so long; no other civilian population so suffered from the horrors of bombardment, starvation, and military action. There are really only two published first-hand accounts that tell this remarkable story of human endurance: Sarah Pryor's *Reminiscences of Peace and War* (1908) and John Herbert Claiborne's *Seventy-five Years in*

Old Virginia (1904). Neither is fully satisfactory; Mrs. Pryor, the wife of a politician-general, was an outsider whose stay in Petersburg was only late in the war, and Dr. Claiborne was serving the military during much of the siege. Thus the experience of the Boisseau family, whose roots in that area were deep and firm, have a unique merit.

One of the more poignant sections of the Boisseau portion of the Pamplin family history has to do with the action at Petersburg on June 9, 1864—known today at "The Battle of Old Men and Young Boys." Through the experiences of Athaliah Boisseau we learn of part, but not all the story. After the war, the women of Petersburg, whose indomitable spirit Athaliah reflected, organized a memorial association to supervise the gathering of Confederate dead from area battlefields and their reburial in the Blandford Cemetery. It soon became a town tradition to honor those who had fallen in its defense with special ceremonies held on June 9. These commemorative activities so impressed a visiting Mrs. John A. Logan, the wife of a Federal general, that she returned north determined to establish a national memorial day. The holiday now celebrated by all Americans owes its beginnings, in part, to the remembrance of Confederate valor by the women of Petersburg.

One of the many figures who come alive in these pages is young Samuel Yates Gilliam. I first came across Mr. Gilliam when I read his testimony, given long after the war, before a U.S. Military Court of Inquiry looking into the Battle of Five Forks. Regarding the "bamboo briars" that so bedeviled the legs of men and horses alike that day, Gilliam said, "It is a green briar; a very tough briar—has little stickers all along on the stem—a long stalk. I have seen fancy canes made of a lot of it." Gilliam's recollections add wonderful rich detail to our understanding of that engagement.

It's an especial joy for any historian to honor individuals who have taken generous and courageous steps to help preserve the physical legacy of our Civil War past. In the fall of 1994 I was privileged to be present when the Pamplin Park Civil War Site first opened its doors to the public. Located on 103 acres of the Boisseau farm at the point of Lee's lines where the celebrated wedge attack by the Union Sixth Corps succeeded in breaking them on the morning of April 2, 1865, Pamplin Park offers a fascinating combination of a state-of-the-art museum and a historic trail featuring some stunningly well-preserved earthworks. Read about the history of this site in Mr. Pamplin's enjoyable dramatized family history and then experience it yourself. It completes the circle in a vital way: from human story to physical site, the ideal way to imbibe history. Everyone with even the slightest interest in the Civil War has ample reason to thank the Pamplin family for this wonderful gift to the American people.

Mr. Trudeau, recently described as "among the first rank of America's narrative historians," is the author of three books: *Bloody Roads South* (1989), *The Last Citadel* (1991), and *Out of the Storm* (1994). The first won the prestigious Fletcher Pratt Award and the second was hailed as the only modern study of the Petersburg campaign. A director for Cultural Programming at National Public Radio, Mr. Trudeau has already written about the Civil War for many publications, including *Civil War Times, America's Civil War,* and *The Military History Quarterly.* Mr. Trudeau lives in the heart of Civil War country in Washington, D.C.

THE PAMPLIN FAMILY AND THE
SIEGE OF PETERSBURG

Prelude to Surrender: The Pamplin Family and the Siege of Petersburg focuses on the American Civil War, and the siege and battles of Petersburg, Va. This is yet another thread in the Pamplin family fabric, namely, the Boisseaus, who owned a plantation outside of Petersburg. The following chronicles and dramatizes the family's remarkable involvement in the Civil War. You will meet the following family members:

Athaliah Goodwyn Boisseau married William Boisseau and had seven children. William, a tobacco inspector and prominent landowner, died in 1838. They owned Tudor Hall, a plantation outside Petersburg, Va., where on their land an assault on Confederate lines took place.

Albert, Joseph and Andrew Boisseau, Athaliah's sons helped her survive and run Tudor Hall during the Civil War.

Ella Boisseau, Athaliah's granddaughter lived with her after her son William and his wife died.

Mary, Albeena and Samuel Gilliam, distant relatives.

Emily and Lewis were the Boisseaus' long-time slaves.

1

ATHALIAH PUT DOWN her sewing and, with a sigh, leaned back in her well-worn arm chair. Her long-time Mammy and maid, Emily, had just brought her some hearty, redolent tea, and before Athaliah tasted the stuff, she let the fragrance carry her back. Back, the soaking, steaming herbs took her: back to when sewing was a social affair and not a financial necessity, to when needles were made of metal and not hawthorn bush barbs. During that long fragrant moment she drifted all the way to the porch of Tudor Hall, her family home in Dinwiddie County. She sat out front of the heavy-linteled doorways of Tudor Hall, at the head of the steep porch steps, sipping afternoon tea. She smiled over far-rippling fields of Virginia cotton and tobacco.

But then Athaliah took her first taste of today's tea.

"Amazing grace!" she exclaimed. "This tastes just awful. Emily, come back here. Come back on *in* here."

Athaliah's kitchen-slave returned to the sewing room. A square-built daughter of Alabama Negroes, Emily had grown more gray than brown.

"Yes'm? she asked.

"Emily, tell me. Just what have you put in this miserable excuse for tea?"

"Sorry ma'am," Emily said. "We all outa sugar. All's left for tea is raspberry leaves."

Emily's honesty was, to be sure, one of the things that had always endeared her to Athaliah. The grandmother and the slave shared a commiserating look—a moment's grim mutual recognition of the times they were in.

"All right Emily," Athaliah sighed, "all right now. Sorry for scolding you, dear. I suppose I just forgot where I was for a moment."

"Yes'm," Emily said. "Hard times, these days."

"Hard, indeed." Athaliah forced down another swallow, then forced up a smile. "Tell me, Emily. Has Lewis come back yet?"

"No ma'am."

"Well, do let me know when he does. We'll need the new provisions for supper tonight."

"Yes ma'am."

Emily turned her back before leaving the sewing parlor, something only the best-loved retainers could do. But Athaliah Goodwyn Boisseau never had been much for master-slave protocol anyway. And now she was old besides, seventy-one, and what had previously been an attractive leanness had turned to miserly skin and bone. Even simple work like sewing took up all the energy she had. Nonetheless, she wanted to sew; she wanted to help out somehow. Sewing brought in cash and barter, essentials in dealing with the terrible hardships brought on by the War Between the States.

Athaliah knew there were still a few pampered aristocrats up in Richmond, a little more than twenty miles north of here. And the wives of those aristocrats would pay dearly for Athaliah's hand-sewn "vanities." Just the year before, hundreds of poor, working-class women, infuriated by rising prices and the scarcity of goods, had gone on a rampage (it was known as the Bread Riot.). They'd smashed store windows and looted food and clothing. President Jefferson Davis had Confederate troops present, but they did not have to take action to disperse the crowds.

"Think of it!" Athaliah had declared at the time. "He has troops there, and all those thousands of poor Southern boys just cut down at Gettysburg!"

"Mama," her son Albert had replied, "times are hard in the cities of our South. I read in the paper—you remember when Vicksburg fell? Vicksburg, in Mississippi? It fell to siege, same time as the Gettysburg battle."

"I remember," Athaliah had snapped. "I read the same reports you did, *Doctor* Boisseau."

Yes, her Albert had been a godsend; yes, he and her other son Andrew had been very generous, putting her up here in this sparsely settled part of Petersburg on Adams Street since she'd moved out of Tudor Hall. And yes, Albert was a learned man, the town surgeon. But she did get tired of him—and Andrew too—treating her with *quite* so much fawning restraint.

"All right, Mama, all right. But before Vicksburg fell? The people there were eating rats."

Athaliah had kept her narrow face set, refusing to squirm.

"Eating rats out of hunger is one thing. But stealing a dress just because you're tired of your old one, that's entirely another."

"It's a scene we'll probably see in more cities," Albert had gone on. "Before this monstrousness ends, we'll see worse than a few windows smashed."

He'd been right, her Dr. Boisseau. In the nine months or so since then more towns had fallen, and now even lovely Atlanta was threatened. Every conquered city seemed to have tales more horrifying than the last. At least the twin railheads of Richmond and Petersburg had been spared till now. And there remained, between the two Fall Line cities, some opportunity for an old woman to help her ever-more-underfed family.

Clever Athaliah had plenty of raw material. She used her own old formal wear: the elegant gowns she'd worn only once to the many balls and social affairs that used to fill up her seasons in and around Petersburg. Silk, velvet, Belgian lace, these and other pretty, frivolous materials—these had been the embroidery of Athaliah's youth. Now she cut them up smaller and smaller, reworking them into fashionable bonnets, scarves, collars, or sleeves. By the spring of 1864, her items were in such demand that all she had to do was send a familiar slave, Lewis, to a few mansions in Richmond. The ladies there knew him, and always had cash and barter on hand.

The barter included such staples as corn and flour, ham and sugar, more valuable than the brown Confederate currency. The price of everything had skyrocketed. Inflation was running at ten percent a month. Flour cost $400 a barrel. So Athaliah persevered with her sewing, even as her own cheeks sank and her own stomach growled. When her old iron and whalebone needles broke from overuse, she made do with the barbs stripped from wild hawthorn. More than once the work drew blood from her dry and bony fingers.

Athaliah would have preferred teaching one of the slaves to do this. But what few slaves the Boisseaus had were either needed back on her Tudor Hall plantation, or had to go foraging around these nearby Petersburg homes of Andrew and Albert. Besides, between the two locations, the family had only nineteen slaves left altogether. Nineteen, out of the hundreds Athaliah had known in her time! Just three days ago, two more had run off.

Athaliah didn't honestly know how she felt about it. The war had forced many a Southern belle to search her soul, regarding how she'd treated the darker peoples of the earth. And Athaliah knew herself well, by this time. She knew that her soul wasn't yet at peace on the subject; she knew she was still searching.

The plantation she'd been born on, the gracious Tudor Hall she'd helped design, even these rooms of Andrew's in Petersburg— all of it, every corner of her life, had been attended by slaves. And like most women of her time and upbringing, Athaliah hadn't herself seen the worst of her serving-people's lives. Oh, she'd read her Exodus and her history books; she knew what slaves had suffered in the past. Part of the tragedy of her beloved South, indeed, was that the cotton- and tobacco-farmers in these states hadn't *invented* slavery, God knows.

The very natives who'd first peopled this land, the Appamatucks and other members of the Powhatan Confederacy, had made slaves of other tribesmen. Likewise, Athaliah's long-ago forebears had owned what were then called "vassals," back in England. Many an old Virginia family had done the same. For instance there were the Bevilles—why, the Bevilles went back to William the Conqueror. William the Conqueror! He'd made slaves of half of England! No question about it, American Southerners hadn't invented the problem. But once slavery had settled into place, there'd been no easy way to get rid of it.

No, Athaliah was no innocent belle. She'd heard of terrible things done in the name of "ownership" She heard of whippings, of parents separated from their children, of feet lopped off to prevent a persistent runaway from trying again. Nonetheless, in all her seventy-one years Athaliah had never been brought face to face with the harsher extremes of what slavery had meant. A plantation mistress didn't go after runaways or attend to their punishment. All Athaliah could say for certain, whenever she found herself agonizing again over this central issue of the war, was that the hardworking men and women who served her were wholly human spirits like herself. Her Emily had a soul, a mind, a place of dreams and frights, just as Athaliah did. When she and Emily shared a look, as they had a minute ago, they shared a common being. And Athaliah's Lewis, too, was made every bit as much in the image of God as herself.

Athaliah knew that much, positively. Her slaves' humanity lay stone-solid at the bottom of her agonizing. And by the same token, she didn't blame them for running off either, in this hard late spring of 1864.

With food in short supply, the slaves got still less than usual. With medicine needed at the front, the slaves received none at all. The Union army was nearby, and now the Bluejackets had started building Negro regiments, training slaves to be soldiers, giving them guns, uniforms, regular meals and ten dollars a month. That was more than enough to lure dozens more slaves off their plantations with every passing week.

"Why, there are days," Athaliah murmured over her sewing, "when I'd leave home *myself* for regular meals and ten dollars a month."

She chuckled, but then grew sober enough to lower her latest piece to her lap. The very thought, she realized, had just brought home to her again the Negroes' humanity. She'd spoken the idea aloud: she'd do what they do.

"Amazing grace," the old woman murmured, even more softly. These were words from a favorite hymn, a song she'd heard once from a West Indian visitor to Tudor Hall.

Amazing Grace: the title rang, the melody sailed, and the lyrics went right to the heart. *How sweet the sound*, the words went, *that saved a wretch like me!* A wretch, yes—that's what the writer declared he'd been, openly and for all to hear. Apparently he'd worked as a ship's captain, this songwriter. Most often he'd been hired for the so-called "Middle Passage," the South Atlantic route that carried the slave ships to and from Africa. He'd run a slave ship, before he'd come to grace.

Athaliah's home plantation was itself something of a wretch, these days. With so few slaves left to work it, Tudor Hall was but a skeleton of its former glory. She and her husband, William Boisseau, had begun building "the Hall" way back in 1812—during an earlier, simpler war. William, a well-regarded Virginia tobacco inspector, combined land he'd purchased with property Athaliah inherited.

The Goodwyns, her parents, had made sure to leave a fair settlement for their girl children as well as the boys; this wasn't feudal England, after all. Thus was created an estate of 1,800 acres, five miles west of Petersburg. The centerpiece was a stunning mansion.

Two and a half stories tall, Tudor Hall had the peaked roofs and heavy-browed gables its name implied. Inside, the main features were the two immense fireplaces, one at each end. The stairways went up steep but wide, with swooping mahogany banisters. Around the place Athaliah and William had planted shade trees: cedar, maple, poplar, magnolia, and dogwood. Also Athaliah's favorite flowers had been put in: azalea, forsythia, and fragrant lilac.

She and her attentive husband had raised seven children in Tudor Hall, five boys and two girls. They'd had a life of enchantment, it seemed to Athaliah now, a life in the sort of Southern high style which was already being called *antebellum*. As a wealthy plantation mother of seven, her weeks had been filled to the bursting with parties, social visits, and sporting events. If she or her William hadn't scheduled some engagement, then young Andrew or Albert or Joseph or William Junior or. ... Lord, just listing them exhausted her! In any case, someone always seemed to have arranged some to-do or other.

Of course, much of that came to an end long before the war. The social whirl Athaliah Boisseau had grown up with was gone forever after 1838—the year her good husband had died. William's death had meant, too, that more of the operation of Tudor Hall fell on the shoulders of Athaliah's sons. They too had needed to quit the Dixie roundelay.

Thus the 1840s had passed without Tudor Hall seeming like too much of a load for Athaliah to bear. Rather it was the next decade, which saw the deaths of two of her sons, that sapped the woman's vitality. In her sixties, she'd sat deathbed vigil for those boys, and arranged every detail of their funerals, too. And there'd been tears, oh Lord yes. Athaliah's tears had seemed dredged up from the bottom of her lungs, after her poor dear boys had passed on.

After that, the woman hadn't the strength for a plantation's demands. She'd moved into Petersburg, into the house of her youngest son, Andrew, anticipating a gentle easing into her own end. Even Andrew's wife Susan was family, after all; in the kind of liaison that was common among the constantly socializing Virginian clans, Andrew had married a cousin, one of Athaliah's nieces.

Another son, Joseph, had stayed on at Tudor Hall to run the plantation. Joseph was married, but he had no children and received some help from another Petersburg brother, Albert. But Albert was the family's most prominent member, and had little time for farming. Not only did he have a thriving medical practice, but also he'd served in the state legislature—until the war.

Now, even in this gloomy spring of 1864, Joseph strove to put down seeds around Tudor Hall as always. But with so few slaves, he could hardly cultivate the entire sprawling three square miles of cropland. In the past, cotton and tobacco had been just about all the Boisseaus had needed to turn a profit, but now running these raw materials out to foreign markets like England or France was next to impossible. The Union blockade deadened even grand old trade centers like Williamsburg—the former "Middle Plantation," for 200 years the center of Virginia's agricultural wealth. And finally, the Confederacy had ordered farmers to plant more food crops. "King Cotton" had been replaced by "King Corn." Or rather, King Cotton was being replaced, slowly, slowly. Too many plantation owners were reluctant to change, even to feed the starving boys in gray.

All in all, Lewis' return today was a terrific relief. First, it did Athaliah good just to see her man make it back safe and sound, stout and smiling, in his hand-sewn, homespun vest jacket. Better still, Lewis told the old woman that her sewing had assured them all of better eating.

"Ma'am, they sho'ly likes your handiwork up there in Richmond," he reported. "I gots even more than 'spected for some of them hats. Coupla sisters kept on raisin' the price, raisin' the price. Thought I was at an auction."

"Amazing grace," Athaliah said. "Lewis, that's just wonderful. Now what were you able to buy?"

"Well, we did all right, did all right. ... 'Fraid the price for some things done gone up again."

"Oh Lord. Naturally."

"Nacherly, yes'm. Nacherly. Yeah but uh, we got us *some*, though. Got us ham peas, some sorghum molasses."

"Sorghum molasses! Oh Lewis, really?"

"Really, ma'am." She and her man shared a smile for a moment, just as earlier she and Emily had shared their sorrow. "I wouldn't mislead ya, ma'am. And we got us a barrel of flour—" the smile grew broader "—a whole *barrel*, too!"

"Amazing grace," Athaliah said. "Molasses and flour. Lewis, I think this calls for Christmas in June. You tell Emily to whip up one of her pecan pies."

"Oh, yes ma'am!" The man grinned still more and gave a body-length nod, practically bowing. But he didn't leave. "Uh ma'am, uh." Lewis' battered fingers played at the lining of his denim vest-jacket. "Uh ma'am, there's one more thing. Yes'm there is." One thick brown hand went under the denim. "Mrs. Armistead, she asked me to give you this."

From under his armpit Lewis fished out a square of paper. This he handed diffidently to squinting Athaliah.

"Lewis, honestly." She kept her look narrow. "Lewis, something like this—why, you took an *awful* risk, bringing me something like this. Some overeager sheriff could've had you arrested for carrying this around."

But Athaliah's gaze softened as she began skimming the news headlines. She realized the twisted irony that made it so dangerous for Lewis to bring her this day-old story. There were laws forbidding slaves to carry paper, even simple blank sheets. The logic behind the law was, slaves might use paper to help them learn to read and write.

After Lewis left, Athaliah read avidly. It was the latest Richmond newspaper. It was two days old: June 6, 1864. The headline shouted *Grant is a Butcher*; the lead story concerned a Union attack on Cold Harbor. Cold Harbor was actually an inland crossroads, not even near a major river, some miles northeast of Richmond. The place was flat, sandy farmland not far from the swampy Chickahominy River. Here the harassed Confederates had dug in, outnumbered about two to one by the Army of the Potomac. For a month now Johnny Reb had undergone a painful, stubborn retreat towards the capital, despite having inflicted terrible casualties. Up in Spotsylvania Court House, and on a battleground called simply The Wilderness, the game troops under Marse Robert had mown down thousands of the Bluecoats, thousands. Still the dogged Ulysses S. Grant, plainly a tougher breed than earlier Federal commanders like McClellan, had kept slogging south. Just a few days ago, according to Athaliah's newspaper, the Yankee general had lost still thousands more of his boys in one fruitless charge after another at Cold Harbor.

With that, Athaliah read, at last the Northern advance seemed to be stopped. In just one month, Robert E. Lee's brave Army of Northern Virginia had cut down close to 50,000 Union troops—more than "the butcher" Grant had lost over the previous three years.

The paper, of course, played up Grant's bloodthirsty desperation, and the courage of the Confederate boys defending their capital. It even claimed that many young Yankees, their enlistment up, actually crawled off the battlefield in the middle of the fight. Yet Athaliah took such reports with a grain of salt by now. No innocent, she recognized the whiff of wartime propaganda. But she could see that both sides were plainly spent, after so much breakneck marching and hell-sent bloodletting. The armies were settling in for what looked like a long-term siege of Richmond. The war wasn't coming any farther south—any closer to home—this year.

Athaliah's reading was interrupted by one of her favorite sounds, namely, the cheery young voice of her granddaughter, Ella. Ella had been born a long way from the Boisseau estates, off in Alabama, where Athaliah's son William had set up a medical practice of his own. William hadn't wanted to compete with his brother Albert, which seemed a sensible decision at the time, and so his six children, including Ella, had started their lives in another part of the South.

But then ten years ago (when this vivacious Ella had been only six) William's wife had taken ill and swiftly died. Another man might have weathered the tragedy, but not William. The doctor couldn't heal his own beset beloved—nor could he save himself, it turned out. Within months the heartbroken William had also died. His children had come to live with Athaliah and the other family in and around Petersburg. Athaliah's deepest joy, in all the hard decade since, had been that Ella had chosen to live with her. Now the teenager burst into the sewing parlor, clutching a large bundle of tatterdemalion plants.

"Grandma, Grandma, look!" Ella exclaimed. "Aren't they just *wild* and delightful?"

"Amazing grace." Athaliah set down her paper, furrowed her brow. "If that isn't the strangest collection of weeds I've ever laid eyes on."

"Oh, Grandma." Ella drooped as she sighed: easy-bodied indeed. "They're not weeds. Honestly! They're medicine."

Behind the girl then came the husky Albert, deliberate and slow as usual. Naturally enough, it was Athaliah's living doctor son who most often took time with her lost doctor's daughter.

"I'm going to help Uncle Albert," Ella went on brightly. "We're going to make medicine and save lives."

"Is that so?" Athaliah looked up skeptically at her sober-sided Albert.

"It's so, Mother," Albert said. "Ella, tell Grandma what we found."

"Oh, yes!" the girl said. Eagerly she sifted through her treasure. "See, these are dandelions, Grandma, you probably already knew that..."

"*Probably?*" Athaliah snapped.

"Oh, yes Grandma, of course you knew." Ella did another endearing body-long droop. "But they're all just so wild and delightful, I quite forget myself! See, this one is pokeweed, this one is, ah, snakeroot. And this..."

The girl paused, studying her latest plant. Then she caught a whiff; she curled up her nose. "*This* is skunk cabbage. It does smell revolting, certainly. But Uncle Albert says it can make medicine, like all the others."

"Lord, Lord," Athaliah said. Her old eyes were fixed again on Albert, skeptically as before.

"Now Mother," he said. He'd had no trouble divining what was in her mind. "These plants can be helpful. You know medicine is in short supply. You know many more of our soldiers die in the hospital than go down on the battlefield. We need to use what we can, Mother. Why, our field hands have been saving each other's lives with this kind of woods medicine for generations now."

"Our field hands?" Athaliah asked.

"Yes. Hands like Lewis and Emily. You know."

The grandmother dropped her head, returning to her long thoughts on slavery.

"The field hands learned it from Indians," Albert went on, more uncertainly. When the old woman didn't respond, he asked: "Mother? Is something wrong?"

"Oh Lord." Bravely she smiled back up at them both. "Is there anything that *isn't* wrong, Albert? That's the question. Take a look at what Lewis brought me," she said, lifting the newspaper from her lap. "Seems General Ulysses S. Grant simply doesn't know when to give up."

Albert read the thing standing up, or tried to. Beside him Ella freed a hand from her flowers and began pulling the paper down from before his face. "Let me see," she said. "Let me see."

Albert struggled to hold the thing close. He was past fifty now, his eyes weak, his hair pepper-and-salt.

"Easy there, young lady," Athaliah put in. "Easy there. It's about time you looked to your studies, I'd say. You pack up this 'medicine' of yours now and go sit down to your own reading."

"Oh Grandma."

"In your room, if you please, young lady."

"But I've already done my reading for this week," Ella protested. "Besides, Mr. Davis says I'm one of his best students."

For all her bobbing and swaying and trying so hard, the youngster wasn't exaggerating. She attended Southern Female College, an elite girls' finishing school, where compliments weren't handed out simply for looking pretty.

The College had been founded on the highest principles in the grim year of 1863. By the beginning of school that September

Vicksburg had fallen and Pickett's Charge at Gettysburg had staked its place in the annals of military disaster.

Yet in a year when these horrors and more were erupting, a man named William Davis had decided to start a school for young women. The man declared his venture a "defiant assertion of civilization in the midst of barbaric carnage." Now Athaliah, mastering her joy at the teenager bouncing before her, tried to follow Davis' gentle example. No reason for Ella to hear today's hard news.

"Young lady," the grandmother said sternly, "this war will end someday. Things *will* return to normal, someday. And when that happens, your education will come in handy, very handy indeed, believe me. Now you get some work done. You go read until supper."

"Oh, Grandma." Yet Ella's last droop, and the way she dragged out of the room—that was an act. Athaliah knew how much the girl enjoyed reading. Ella's special favorites were stories about the far West, about Oregon Trail pioneers and all the adventure beyond the Mississippi. Today's jaunt in the woods, too, had been an expression of the same girlish enthusiasm for the wild. When she left the sewing parlor, she took with her the raw odor of her bunched herbs.

"I see," Albert said, able to finish the paper at last, "I see." He looked up from the report, the deep-set wrinkles round his eyes revealing again how much the last few years had taken out of him.

"Mother, I trust you see through the Richmond bias here." He gestured at the headline. "Grant may be a butcher. But that doesn't mean the Confederacy's going to win the war. What does it matter if Grant loses a thousand of his troops a day? The next day, two thousand more march down and replace them."

"Albert. Is this a doctor's diagnosis?"

"Mother, yes. This is a doctor refusing to deny what he can see as plainly as these headlines—" he flipped over the newspaper clipping in his hand "—before his face. The question is no longer whether we will lose. The question is whether it will happen without coming into our home."

Athaliah narrowed her eyes. Albert was frightened, of course. And Andrew too, and Joseph: they were all past fifty and exempted from being conscripted, but they were frightened nonetheless. Indeed, the same fear now gripped any Southern man who, for whatever reason, had been excused from military service. As the fighting appeared to be coming home—as the Yankee general Sherman, outside Atlanta, spoke of something called "total war"— these homebound men had to face the same horrifying possibilities as the soldiers in the ranks had been living with since the first Bull Run.

"Mother," Albert went on, "we must be realistic. Do you realize the hostilities could come to our very *doorstep?*"

"We all do, Albert. We all do. Amazing grace, we'll see it through somehow."

Her stocky, full-grown son met her eyes again. Heavily he sighed, a rueful smile stretching between his salted muttonchops. His posture relaxed; he laid a hand on her worn-down shoulder. "The question," he repeated more gently, "is whether it will reach us down here?"

"Lord, yes," Athaliah agreed. "But that's not the most important question."

Her son frowned, tugging at a muttonchop.

"The most important question," the grandmother said, "is how did it come to this? What have we done wrong?"

The next morning Albert rose early. He crossed the yard to his brother's kitchen, as usual these days, since the only house help either son had left were Athaliah's two. Still enjoying the fullness of last night's pecan pie, Albert did his best to drink down what now passed for coffee in the South.

"Emily, really," Albert said. "What is this concoction?"

"Rosie over at Miz Taylor's give me the recipe, Dr. Boisseau." The woman always sounded more deferential with her mistress' son than with Athaliah herself. "It's got chicory, dried peas, and beets. Don't you think it's better than that okra and corn?"

"It's strange brew indeed, Emily."

The gray woman remained quiet, waiting.

"But then, we're all sipping strange brews across the South, aren't we? These days we'd better get used to brews of an entirely different kind."

Emily didn't respond. The doctor took one last sip, grimaced, then gave his instructions: "No need to set a place for me tonight, Emily. I'll dine at Tudor Hall this evening." He went out, headed for the back door.

The doctor had been gone for no more than an hour, and the rest of the household hardly had time to judge Emily's latest "coffee," when he came bursting back in. Albert came through the front door this time, breathless after the sprint from his carriage.

"The Yankees," he gasped. "They're coming!"

Athaliah and the rest rushed out of the dining room, gathering around him and—trailing the doctor in the door—Lewis, that day's coachman. Though the news was hardly good, young Ella couldn't keep from bobbing round the edge of the crowd, like a girl at a carnival.

"The Yankees!" Albert kept repeating. "They're here already, by God. They're just outside the city."

"Are you sure?" Athaliah asked. "They're supposed to be up by Cold Harbor."

Then the clanging of the courthouse bell broke into their hubbub. Several church bells took up the warning next, tolling away as if men were dying already.

"*Now* do you believe me?" Albert asked, showing again the fearful anger of the night before. "The Yankees are everywhere, I tell you. They're up in Cold Harbor and they're down here as well."

Athaliah's thin lips drew narrower still. "We've got to get ready to leave. We may not have much time."

Ella shoved up beside her, bobbing. "Why would we have to leave?"

"Ella, Lord, Lord!" the grandmother said, exasperated. "Go gather up a case of clothing. One case, only! Albert, you—"

But her son was already making the arrangements, conferring with Emily and Lewis as the three of them hurried together towards the kitchen.

Outside, at first distant but then closing in, gunfire crackled as the ninth day of June, 1864, wore on. By late afternoon several Union regiments stood at the edge of town. The Bluejackets appeared wary of the Petersburg fortifications but nonetheless ready to fight, even after their hard ten-mile ride south. The town's only defenders, meantime, were 125 boys as young as sixteen and men as old as sixty-one. Though Albert was far too old for this sort of thing, his heart still felt a tug when he thought of the men defending the city.

The man responsible for this motley band was himself something of an outcast: the former Governor of Virginia, Henry Wise. As Governor, five years before the war, he'd called for Virginia to secede from the Union. He had no military training and so had been sent to Petersburg mostly to keep him out of harm's way. Yet it was Wise's clever strategy that would hold off a much larger and better equipped Union cavalry for several hours.

Slaves had dug out some ten miles of earthworks, trenches, gun emplacements, and other fortifications for the city. Now, though Wise's defenses lacked the troops to fill them—he was outnumbered a good ten to one—he spread his ill-equipped soldiers under the command of Major Fletcher T. Archer along the entire range of defensive battlements, ordering that there be ten feet between each man. After that, he kept shifting them from location to location, creating the illusion of a much larger army.

The trick was a politician's, rather than a military man's. Nonetheless, Grant's shock troops came within 150 yards of the city streets. Their last barrier was a deep ravine, and there Colonel Archer bunched his ragtag men for a true defensive stand.

Meantime, Athaliah and the rest of her family loaded their buggy with provisions and prepared to ride west to Tudor Hall, away from the invasion. But as Wise's ruse continued to hold up the Northerners' advance, they chose to wait. Albert took up a position two blocks away, on a hill, where he could watch the battle. Early in the afternoon, with the Bluejacket swarms seemingly unstoppable, Albert ran down the hill once more and declared it was time to go. "Time," he shouted, "*time!*" But no sooner had Athaliah and the others piled up into the buggy than Confederate reinforcements began at last to reach the town.

The boys in gray came streaming down the Petersburg byways, moving at a trot after who knows how many hours of forced marching. As they came they shrieked, raising their massed voices in the infamous Rebel Yell, and even the discouraged Albert couldn't help but roar back, heartened by so many brave boys arriving in the very nick of time.

But these Confederate saviors were, on closer inspection, a sorry sight. Gaunt, bloody, ragged, exhausted, and often carrying only an improvised excuse for a weapon, these artillery and cavalry men bore the devastation of month after month of unrelenting warfare. Indeed, for some of them it had been year after year of this inferno—yet most were young enough to be Athaliah's grandchildren. Every now and then there passed a boy she knew from around Petersburg, but as he hustled by, the old woman would barely recognize him. Where did these battle-weary scarecrows find the energy for that infamous Yell? Drawn-out and yet sharply punctuated, hideous and yet courageous, Johnny Reb's holler never failed to inspire terror in the Bluejackets across the way.

The old woman herself wasn't up to anything like that, but she did what she could. "God bless you all!" Athaliah cried. "Amazing grace!"

Her shout elicited a few more yells from the passing hundreds. They kept bravely trotting by, making for the earthworks and the massing invaders.

Near the Boisseau house at Poplar Lawn, the park where the defenders mustered their troops, two smaller groups split off from the ranks. These were artillery, with horse-drawn caissons. These squads maneuvered cannons to the tops of two close-by hillsides. By then the Union cavalry had begun to work their way up the side of the city's last defensive ravine. Henry Wise's threadbare defense had only been able to do so much. But now the reinforcements got into it, their hilltop batteries unleashing a horrific volley. Deafening, skull-thumping, every blast seemed to suck all the air out of the surrounding city. From her buggy Athaliah could see Andrew's windows bulge and rattle, and all round her flocks of birds startled up hysterically.

Above the din, the old woman heard someone shouting. "Head for the cellar!" Then as she clambered from the carriage, Athaliah realized it was she who'd been shouting. Seventy-one years old, frail and breathless, she'd fallen back on some naked urge for survival. She'd ordered everyone to shelter.

The Boisseaus and their two slaves scrambled into the big home's English basement, half above ground and half below, and huddled there for the rest of the afternoon. Down there, in the dark and the banging and the smell of sulfur, it was unlike anything Athaliah had ever known. She'd had no real idea of what war was like—no notion of the shape, the feel, the impact of the end of the world. The obscure monsters of Revelation hadn't prepared the old woman.

After a while Athaliah noticed that Emily and Lewis appeared to be the quietest, the least shaken. Even the irrepressible Ella cringed, quivering in Albert's embrace, her hands clamped to the sides of her young face. But the two slaves sat reserved, hands on knees, their old mouths firm. Could they have seen something like this before? Or—Athaliah found herself wondering—had poor black Emily and Lewis seen worse?

Then Athaliah had to get out. She couldn't stand the hard thoughts that crowded in on her, down in that battle-shaken cellar: the guilt, the shame. She couldn't stand to be so enclosed, held back, enslaved—she didn't deserve it! And Albert didn't have hands enough to stop her.

The old woman was up and out of there in a moment. She emerged into sunlight streaming through cannon smoke, the triumphal cries of Southerners echoing through their city. The Confederate cannons had done their work—the Union cavalry had fled. Athaliah saw the blue-uniformed horsemen galloping away out of range of the big guns. Could she call them *enemies*? She knew those were boys over there too, boys and families. And most of those Union families had at one point or another in the past shared some loving kinship, some cousin or girlfriend or partner in trade, with the families she knew on this Confederate side. The grandmother was watching war between her own children, and her heart filled with sorrow to think that too often the most intense and longest lasting hatred is stirred between brothers.

And here she was, upright in her front yard—Athaliah Goodwyn Boisseau, lifelong slaveholder, staring clear-eyed at the last of the horror her own way of life had created. She hadn't invented slavery, neither she nor the demure minions like her, the respectable and liquid-voiced ladies with their blood and background and ingrained gentility of heart. Yet the horror Athaliah saw now had been lurking all the while behind that gentility; the chained-down human spirits on which her world had been built had broken free at last, vengeful and bloodthirsty. Indeed, those chained spirits had been waiting since long before Athaliah's world had been built— the South hadn't invented slavery, she told herself yet again. Rather the long-confined wretched of the earth had been climbing this way for millennia now: misery had been climbing the centuries. Was there no end to it? Athaliah wondered. Was there *nothing* but misery, climbing the centuries?

"Amazing grace," she whispered, through seeping tears. "Amazing grace."

The Petersburg reinforcements threw back the Union assault, forcing them south. After that General P.G.T. Beauregard took command over the Rebel troops defending Petersburg, which now numbered far fewer than 57,000. But then the Union's Grant defied logic, or so it seemed to the Confederacy's Lee. The bulldog Northerner ordered a march south from Richmond; with 112,000 Union troops, he prepared a full-scale attack on the well-entrenched Petersburg.

Grant reasoned that most food and essentials coming into Richmond had to go through the southern railhead, and to choke off supplies there would be easier than taking the Confederate capital by force. Army of the Potomac engineers threw a 2,100-foot pontoon bridge over the James River in only eight hours. Then the hundred-thousand-strong juggernaut lurched southward again, toward Petersburg. By June 9, the assault group began keeping the city's defenders busy.

Petersburg had been, till then, a quiet place: bright Richmond's more restrained little sister. Streets here were orderly and tree-lined, houses tidy and unpretentious. The Boisseau homes had small front yards surrounded by low wrought iron. And if you could measure a town's religious character by the number of its church steeples, Petersburg must have been very close to God.

Like Athaliah Boisseau, most residents must have seen war's coming as some horrible act of God. If their city had been wicked, they'd never seen it; if they themselves had been sinning, they'd never known it. But now, just six days later, the Union advance troops mounted another, still larger attack. And again the Confederate defenses were reed thin, terribly outnumbered.

But the Yanks, as before, never pressed their advantage. One mile-long fortification east of the city fell to the Bluejacket infantry, which included a division of the U.S. Colored Troops, freed slaves led by white officers. And this was a key fortification, a linchpin. Once the Negro infantry stormed into it, nearly every remaining soldier in gray knew that Petersburg lay open—Petersburg and no doubt the capital of the Confederacy as well. Yet once again, the Union generals preferred to remain cautious. A secondary assault was ordered to wait until scouts could determine how strong the Confederate defenses were. Night fell on eerie quiet. And this respite—which stretched into several more days—gave General Beauregard time to call up more reinforcements and build additional trenches and earthworks.

What the Federal forces failed to take by action, they would try to gain by waiting. Both sides began to settle into siege warfare, a war of attrition, alternately boring and horrendous. And eventually even Grant—though at first furious at his generals' missed opportunity—realized that time was the Union's ally. His engineers set up a command center at City Point, at the junction of the James and the Appomattox, eight miles to the northeast.

Athaliah Boisseau, hearing of the new military headquarters, shook her head. Why, it was over near her old friends the Bevilles! That God-fearing, well-spoken family too was being shown the face of misery and sin. To what end? the old woman wondered. If these days were the Revelation for people like the Boisseaus and the Bevilles, then what Kingdom of God lay behind the moment's ruling shame?

Over at City Point the Army of the Potomac built a mile of wharves, an immense tent hospital, and row upon row of supply houses. Within a few short months "the Point" became one of the world's busiest seaports, handling 200 ships a day. The ships carried men, munitions, and food; the troops and material traveled to Petersburg via a brand new Army-built railroad line. The City Point bakeries pumped out 123,000 loaves of fresh bread daily; the delivery system brought it to the Bluejacket soldiers still warm from the ovens. The Army of the Potomac had every luxury warfare allows.

The Boisseaus learned all this over the next several weeks. Indeed, Athaliah, struggling to find some good in her infernal vision of brother against brother, proved a quick study in problems of military supply and movement. The Union lines, she learned, remained about a mile off. Thus, during the third week of June, she and her family could still leave the city by going west to Tudor Hall or north to Richmond. But what Athaliah and her kin didn't know, during those first days of digging in, was that the Army of the Potomac had brought in three devastating new weapons.

These soon made their presence felt. One morning before month's end, Athaliah, Ella, Andrew, and his wife Susan had gathered as usual in the dining room, doing their best to manage a siege city's miserable excuse for breakfast.

"Uncle Albert is right," Ella said, over Emily's makeshift coffee. "This is indeed strange brew."

Wanly, Athaliah smiled. The girl remained a godsend, making jokes and hoping for the best. But Ella's teenage optimism had changed its focus; the granddaughter was struggling to become more practical.

"Well, Grandma," she went on, "I suppose this queer stuff will give me the energy to do more sewing. I mean, you and I must keep going with that."

"Indeed we must," Athaliah said. "We need to send Lewis back up to Richmond soon..."

An eerie whistling cut her off; a rumble rattled the windows. Albert looked towards the more densely settled part of the city and saw a cloud of smoke and dust rising. The family sat immobile at first, stunned, wordless.

"Wh-what?" Andrew began, reaching for his wife.

But once again the whistling came: a hunter's piercing signal to his bird dog, but metallic and inconceivably loud.

"The cellar! Everyone, quickly—the *cellar!*" At least this time Athaliah knew it was she who was yelling. Before they reached the cellar door, however, another muffled explosion came from city center; in the distance she glimpsed the wall of a house collapsing. Another family blasted to shreds. But Athaliah had enough of battle-field Revelation, for now. Though her family was out of range of Union artillery, nonetheless she forced herself to join the others in the root cellar. Once more they huddled in the herb-rich dark, arms linked, heads down. The banging they knew—but what was this diabolical new *whistling?*

"Strange brew," Ella repeated, during a lull. She was trying to smile, fixing crooked lips across a pale, frightened face.

Hollowly Andrew laughed. Athaliah, for her part, kept trying to blink away her vision of ancient injustices working towards redress.

"Every time there's an explosion," Ella went on, "I see the queerest things."

"That so, chile?" Emily said. She and Lewis had remained as calm as before, voiceless in the dark.

"Oh yes, Mammy Emily," the teenager went on. "The queer-est things, honestly. They flash before my eyes bold as you please."

Athaliah, startled, stroked the girl's hair. "Amazing grace, my sweet Ella."

The pretty youngster turned her crooked smile the grandmother's way. "Amazing...grace?" she asked. "Do you mean you see such things, too?"

Andrew cut in, sounding sober as his big brother Albert. "Hellfire and damnation," he said. "That's what I see. Every time another of those bombs goes off, I see the Devil laughing in Hell."

"My son, my granddaughter," Athaliah said. "Please." Even she was surprised at the unexpected gravity in her voice. "Please," she repeated. "Whatever God gives us to see, he also gives us to com-prehend."

Finally the shelling stopped and the family emerged once more into the sunlight. "Lord ha' mercy," Emily declared, then. "Is it still 'fore lunch time?" Athaliah laughed at that, heartened by what she saw. They'd all expected devastation, the utter ruin of their city, but in fact the damage appeared slight. The Dunlops had lost half their chimney wall, but all in all Petersburg seemed to have survived this first major artillery barrage of the siege.

"Lunch?" Lewis asked Emily, incredulous. "Big mama, you thinkin' bout *lunch?*"

Athaliah laughed again, more deeply, and this time her son and granddaughter joined in.

The barrage the Boisseaus and the rest of Petersburg had endured, they found out over the next few days, included some shelling from the "Dictator." This new "Dictator" had to travel mounted on a flat-bed rail car, it was such an ungainly weapon. Essentially a stubby mortar, it could hurl 200-pound exploding shells more than two miles.

General Grant's strategy had become to wear down Petersburg's citizens. It was a strategy he'd used effectively in the siege of Vicksburg the year before. So the Army of the Potomac lobbed artillery into Petersburg at unpredictable times, hitting all sorts of different targets, the shells whistling with varying intensities. But Petersburg's citizens—despite all their losses, their deprivations, their bad dreams—adjusted and went on with their lives. They learned to gauge the whistle of incoming artillery, to watch for the burning fuses of the cannonballs. In this way even the man on the street could predict where the shells would strike; they could know whether to take shelter or not. The Boisseaus soon appointed Ella to this watch duty, since the active youngster had the sharpest eyes.

For the troops at the front lines, however, it was a different story. Life in the trenches combined excruciating tedium and horrifying fear. In some places the opposing forces' trenches were no more than fifty yards apart, close enough to carry on conversations—or hurl insults and promises of a painful death. Meanwhile, rifles were so powerful and accurate that to lift one's head above the earthworks was to risk certain death. Soldiers built walls of sandbags with slits for their rifles, but even these could be unsafe. Snipers simply waited for an enemy head to block off the daylight behind the slit.

Next, Grant's well-stocked army introduced a second weapon that changed the face of war. It too had a sound like nothing else heard before in combat: a grating *rat-a-tat-tat-tat*, grinding on endlessly. It was, in effect, a rifle that didn't need to pause for loading, a whole rapid-firing rifle squad contained in a single emplacement. The new killing tool was called the Gatling gun, after its inventor, though those in the trenches called it by a simpler name: machine gun. A prototype had been tried at Gettysburg, and its use in Petersburg, though limited to a few emplacements, was still enough to spread fear.

Still, Robert E. Lee's lines didn't budge. Trench warfare was proving static; even an undermanned, undergunned group could hold out indefinitely, so long as it maintained open supply lines. Life within the fortifications was by and large miserable, yes. Soldiers suffered from the Virginia heat, the persistent rats, the mindless tedium. But Petersburg remained in Confederate hands. So Grant's commanders came up with yet another new weapon, the third of this extraordinary campaign.

Petersburg had lived under siege for nearly two months, by the time this weapon was tried. By then—the end of July—Tudor Hall had brought in some crops at least, and the generous Boisseaus had tithed the Confederacy and their neighbors. In town, Athaliah and Andrew and Albert and the others had developed something resembling regularity, despite their unnaturally disrupted lives. Though the enemy artillery barrages continued day and night, Athaliah and her family had learned to sleep through most of them. But just before dawn, July 30, all of them were jerked from their beds by an explosion like nothing they'd ever heard before.

The blast went off at 4:40 a.m.; Athaliah, as was her habit, looked first at the clock. The thunder of detonation was so loud, even though it was toward the front, she wouldn't have been surprised if lightning had struck their backyard. Or was the lightning *underground*? The earth was shaking and it was raining dirt, gravel, scraps of wood and debris over the city. Lightning underground, earth overhead: it was the world turned upside down.

What had waked the old woman was a Union assault unlike any ever attempted. Miners from Pennsylvania had dug a 500-foot tunnel under Confederate lines. At the end of the tunnel they'd paced four tons of black powder; at 4:40 a.m., they'd lit the fuse.

The plan was to rupture the fortifications and, before the surrounding Rebels could refill the gap, send Federal shock troops through. The crater left by the explosion was immense, thirty feet deep and seventy feet across. An entire Confederate fort had collapsed into the hole, with nearly 300 men killed on the spot. For hundreds of yards on either side, Rebel soldiers scuttled back in amazement, in dread. Yet then, incredibly, it took nearly fifteen minutes for the Union troops to enter the crater. One of the division commanders assigned to the attack was back in the bomb-proof dirt shelters. One of the scrappy divisions of the U.S. Colored Troops, already seasoned and eager for more action, had been originally slated to make the first assault. But Grant feared that if the assault was a failure, it would appear that the government cared nothing for the blacks and sacrificed them. At the last moment the Colored Troops had been pulled back, replaced by far more exhausted whites.

When Union troops finally approached the pit, they arrived more curious than anything else. Unable to get around it, they clambered in—into what one survivor called "a cauldron of hell," trapped hopelessly under the guns of a furious Confederate rally. Belatedly, desperately, Federal commanders sent in the Colored Troops, and these fought with the bravery of men who have nothing to lose, often going hand to hand in the blown-apart muck. Here and there they even broke through the Confederate line, but they couldn't by themselves overcome several hours of inept management.

Union casualties were enormous. Though the battle had begun with the slaughter of 300 Secessionists, by its end the Army of the Potomac had lost 3,800 men at the battle of the Crater, twelve or thirteen times as many as the Confederates lost in the initial blast. On the Confederate side, fewer than a thousand died overall. General Grant called the episode "the saddest affair I have ever witnessed in the war." But again it was Grant who took the blame in the press, branded a butcher once more. Stung, exasperated, the Federal commander resorted again to siege. His campaign returned to a series of offensives designed to capture the various supply routes leading into Petersburg. He slowly burrowed west around the city, extending his lines and forcing Lee to spread his threadbare troops even more thinly. By September those lines reached Tudor Hall.

Athaliah's son Joseph and his wife Ann had remained childless since inheriting Tudor Hall a few years before the War. They lavished their affections instead on the land, the livestock, the slaves and their families. They were old-style Virginians, in love with farming and the countryside.

By late summer, the Union's continual westward probing had seen some five forward fortifications put up within a mile and a half of Tudor Hall. Not long after that Joseph Boisseau was interrupted at breakfast by a stern knock at his stately front doors. In years past, a slave would have answered. But no longer. Joseph Boisseau left his plate of fatback and went to the door himself.

His caller was no farmer. For today's visit this Confederate officer—for that's what the man at the door was, plainly—had pulled on his parade uniform, the elegant gray jacket with gold trim, gold buttons, a gold sash and a long gold-tipped saber. All this, Joseph understood after a moment, was out of respect to the grandeur of the house. Joseph himself stood a little more erect, tucking back his gray beard. But the visitor's regal garb didn't mask his fatigue. On second glance Joseph could tell that this was a man weary of battle, struggling to fulfill his obligations in the face of growing discouragement and dwindling supplies.

The officer introduced himself as a South Carolina General. "Samuel McGowan, sir," he said, "Do you mind if I come in?"

"Please." Joseph tried to match the officer's formal *politesse.* "Would you care to join us for some, ah, some hot breakfast drink?"

McGowan seemed dumbfounded at the generosity. As the men moved toward the kitchen, Joseph could swear he heard his visitor's stomach growl. And once Joseph's wife had poured the Carolinian a cup of their own substitute for coffee, he drank it down without regard for what it was made of. Clearly, this was a man who'd grown used to strange brews.

The soldier took some fatback as well. Not till he'd taken three or four hurried, hungry bites did McGowan at last remember his business. He'd come, he said swallowing, to ask the two of them to make "a sacrifice."

GENERAL SAMUEL McGOWAN

"Many have made such sacrifices for the Confederacy," he said. "Many."

Ann and Joseph exchanged anxious glances. Both knew what was coming.

"You've heard the skirmishes going on near here, no doubt," the officer went on. "You've seen the Yankee forts nearby. That devil Grant wants to find some way to cut the railroads leading from Petersburg, since he can't break through our brave boys in front of the city."

"You want our farm," Joseph blurted.

"We cannot allow the Yanks into Petersburg. We simply cannot. Once he gets into Petersburg, our capital's but a train ride away. Your plantation," McGowan continued more gently, "well, its location is strategic, to say the least. Boydton Plank Road out there—" he gestured towards the parlor windows "—is the most important supply route into the city, and it stands between Grant and the vital South Side Rail Road."

"General McGowan," Ann said, "we are no strategists."

"Ah, but you understand the need for food, don't you? You understand the need for regular supplies? We desperately need the Rail Road, and we need the Boydton Plank Road, as well."

"How much do you want?" Joseph asked, his heart sinking. "You see we don't have much." With a shaky hand he indicated his wife and himself, sitting in the servants' side of the house, eating food they'd prepared themselves.

"We need your sacrifice for the Confederacy," the Carolinian said, more gently still. "We need your land, your house, everything." His voice seemed almost to age into greater kindness. "Mr. Boisseau, I'm very sorry. But the war has come to your plantation. It has come to so many, you know."

"You need *everything*?" Joseph asked, angry.

The general turned businesslike. "We need to build defensive positions, and we plan to use your house for a hospital. We need not move into your home at once, but there will soon be hundreds of soldiers living on your property."

"Everything," Joseph repeated, angry still. But his rage, he realized, was directed mostly at himself, at his own childish yearning to burst into tears and beg for some reassurance. Lord, he thought, we are fragile.

"General," he went on, striving to master himself. "General, we do have one request."

The soldier met his eyes, levelly.

"This home means the world to us," Joseph said. "My parents built it more than fifty years ago, my sisters and brothers were born here, we all grew up here. My request is—" again he struggled for control "—please treat it with care."

McGowan said he'd do what he could, formal as ever, straightening his buttons and sash. But after he'd remounted his horse and left, Ann and Joseph needed several minutes arm in arm on the front porch, gazing out over their beloved Tudor Hall. It was still harvest time and their slaves were hard at work picking cotton, tobacco, and vegetables. The sunlight filtered through a haze of dust kicked up by the workers. Joseph remembered how his mother Athaliah used to love such scenes—how she'd sit in her rocker on an afternoon, sipping the real tea they'd had before the war, smiling over the tranquil fields. Yet now there was nothing tranquil; from where he stood, Joseph could hear gunfire. Would this be the last time a Boisseau stood on that porch, looking over land he was happy to call his own?

Before midday, Confederate soldiers began arriving. Engineers walked along a steep ravine across the property, a natural defensive bulwark, and there staked out a lien for fortifications. Earthworks were built fifteen feet across, wide enough to absorb Union artillery. Trenches went deep enough for troops to stand with their heads out of harm's way, while at the same time keeping a clear view of approaching forces. The Rebels cut down trees and made sharpened stakes to plant pointed end up, a bristling infantry obstacle called *abatis and fraise*. Cannons rolled into place. Tudor Hall became an armed camp.

Yet even this late in the war, officers of the Confederacy did what they could to maintain some semblance of Southern civility and grace. Through the frightening nights that followed, General McGowan and his high command proved surprisingly genial guests. The perceptive South Carolinian could see that the Boisseaus felt more and more like strangers in their long-time family home, and he tried his best to rekindle the spirit of Tudor Hall. McGowan and the other generals enjoyed many a long hour of whist, joking and laughter around the dinner table. Some nights, before the fireplace, the Boisseaus and their visitors listened rapt as McGowan recited poems of Milton or whole passages from Shakespeare. There wasn't much light to read by, and few books other than the Bible had survived the family's need for items of barter.

Still, despite the comfort of these evenings, every day the Hall felt less like a home. McGowan said that Grant's attack would come, paradoxically, from the south, and so before long Joseph and Ann packed what they could and moved the opposite way, north toward the still-tranquil Appomattox River.

Lewis' trips to Richmond had become less and less productive, as winter settled in. Prices kept skyrocketing, and more than a few unscrupulous shop owners refused even to sell some products, waiting another day or so for prices to rise still more. Basic foods such as beans and rice were available, but many things now became luxuries out of most people's reach.

Life for the soldiers was worse. The winter of 1864-1865 proved one of the coldest in memory. Sleet and snow turned the trenches into quagmires. The mud, sometimes two feet deep, alternately froze and thawed, creating a sickening slop. And despite the miserable conditions, the work of war had to continue. Confederate soldiers tried tunneling out mines of their own, as the Federals had done last July, but they never got far enough to blow any of them up.

Rations, meantime, were cut to a pint of cornmeal a day. Soldiers sometimes went for a week or more without meat. The Federals had received issues of warm overcoats for the winter, but they had no specific seasonal uniform. Confederates received very little. Plus in winter as in summer, the stench that ruled their days was a combination of latrines impossible to clean and bodies impossible to bury.

Many deserted, many, as sober and clear-eyed about the Confederacy's doom as Albert Boisseau. Up to several hundred a day fled the Petersburg entrenchments. And this dispirited dwindling was, of course, just what Grant and his commanders had been counting on.

Those Confederates who remained tried to keep their spirits high. When they received their pay (typically, four months late), they spent with abandon. Petersburg dance halls and taverns did a booming trade. And when the Confederate dollars ran out, they bartered for goods. Indeed, in one of the most bizarre developments of a campaign like no other before it, Johnny Reb bartered with Yank, trading goods between the opposing lines. There was an unwritten agreement that soldiers from both sides could hold swap meets in a few designated places, and that at such times no shots would be fired. It was during those exchanges that the two sides' contrast in supply became abundantly clear. The Federal soldiers had everything they wanted, the Confederates much less— and still less reason to stay and fight.

That November, President Abraham Lincoln declared a national holiday of Thanksgiving to be held on the last Thursday of the month. Union soldiers celebrated with a feast of turkey or chicken, pies and fruit. The Confederates, meantime, had their usual corn-meal. But both sides, in a poignant show of honor between mortal combatants, declared a single-day cease fire.

These stories of humanity in the midst of horror, of compassion in an inferno, touched Athaliah Boisseau most deeply in the last days of her life. Her household, after all, hardly had it easier than the troops at the front. Tudor Hall was gone, Tudor Hall and all it had offered.

"Amazing grace," Athaliah murmured, when the reserved Albert brought the news about the Hall. "It's bad as Petersburg over there."

The old woman was spending most of her days in bed by now. During her talk with Albert she sank back into the pillows, too sick to take the news sitting up. "The Lord does take everything," she told her son, "doesn't he?"

"Oh, Mother," Albert said, broken-voiced. "I wondered if I should tell you at all."

"No, I'm glad you told me," the old woman said. "I needed to know." Though too weak to raise her head again, she fixed him with a dead-serious look. "You think the soldiers in the trenches here have the truth hidden from them?"

Albert eyed her worriedly, a doctor once more.

"The soldiers know the truth," Athaliah said. "They've looked the worst in the face. And I must too."

Albert called for Ella, and told the girl to bring the best tea they had left, plus any kind of fruit. Ella by then had begun to work with Lewis on foraging after food, making a startling combination of spunky white youth and canny black age. They proved a re-markably successful twosome, but even Ella and Lewis had trouble finding meat during that hard winter. The Boisseaus, like many others, had to live with a diet of cornbread and black-eyed peas.

Now the girl came running up the steep stairs with an herb tea she'd learned about from Emily and an apple from the relatively unaffected orchards north of town.

"Ella, Lord," Athaliah said, after the youngster had given her a few sips of the tea. "You are a godsend."

Albert took out his pocketknife and cut up the apple. Together he and the teenager got some nourishment into the grandmother, and in a few minutes Athaliah was sitting up again. Albert tried to bring up one of the happier times he remembered from the old days at the Hall, a harvest dance when father William had insisted on scratching off the names of everyone else on Athaliah's card. But his mother didn't want to lose herself in the past. Instead she asked Ella to sit beside her on the bed and, taking the girl's hand, declared she wanted to know if Ella still "saw things" when the Union bombs landed nearby.

"Sometimes," Ella said, bobbing a bit as she nodded.

"And does your Uncle Andrew," the old woman asked, "still claim to see hellfire and damnation?"

Ella frowned, and shared a look with Albert. But Athaliah kept her fingers tightly meshed with the girl's, her look kind but free of jokes.

"We mustn't flee the hellfire we see," she told her granddaughter, there in her faded bedroom. "We mustn't, because it comes from within us. It is a part of us."

"Mother..." Albert began.

"Albert, *please*." For a moment she was the disciplinarian of Tudor Hall again, certain of the rules and brooking no impertinence. "I'm not some doddering, dying fool, Albert." Athaliah coughed and sank into her pillows once more. But she maintained her grip on Ella's hand, and she took them both in with an unshaken look.

"Dying?" Ella asked. "Grandma, you're not—"

"Of course I'm dying," Athaliah snapped. "I know that, of course. But because I know that, I also know something more." Her look remained tough, a soldier's, but her voice grew more gentle. "I know, too, that the hellfire is within us. And the grace to overcome it is within us as well. The grace to overcome *anything*, children."

"You mean," Albert tried, "just as our Southern system contained its own fatal flaw..."

Athaliah nodded. "Just as our beloved South contained the seeds of its own destruction, in the wounds and injustice we laid on poor souls like Emily and Lewis, so we each in us contain a horror, a wretchedness, a hellfire."

Ella squeezed the old woman's hand. "But I'm working with Lewis now, Grandma. He's no slave to me, that wonderful old man."

Albert stared at his bouncing niece, blinking. Yes, she was the new breed, and every generation must give way to the new breed. But it still took a man by surprise, when he saw it taking place right there before him.

"Why, without Lewis," Ella went on, "we'd starve."

"And knowing that," Athaliah said, "recognizing that, is the power of grace within us. Amazing grace, how sweet the sound. It is the power that keeps these soldiers in our trenches human and rich in soul, though every day they face a hellfire worse even than we do."

"Amen to that," Albert said quietly. "I see the poor wretches in surgery. Never seen such strength of souls. Tell them they're going to die in the next ten minutes, they never utter a word of complaint."

"Lord, no," Athaliah said. "And I'm not going to start complaining now, either. Not when out there—" she cocked her chin towards her window "—there are soldiers in gray and soldiers in blue..."

"Soldiers with black faces," Ella put in, "and soldiers with white faces."

"Lord, yes," Athaliah said. "And all of them, all of them keeping their spirits alive through inferno after inferno, by the power of God's amazing grace."

"Amazing grace," Albert echoed, a deep sadness coming into his look.

But Ella repeated the words with a laugh, and bent to hug her dying grandmother.

Athaliah died in early December, a bitterly cold time when the Boisseaus' fireplaces were barely enough even for young Ella. On the eighth of the month, during a Union barrage aimed at the

Boisseaus' neighborhood, the old woman refused Andrew's offer to carry her down to the cellar.

"It's nothing but a lot of strange colors and smells and noises," she told her son. "Nothing but a strange brew. That's all these bombardments are."

"Mother..." Andrew began.

"Go," she said. "Save your worrying for Ella."

And young Ella was the first to discover her afterward. Athaliah was upright at her headboard, her sewing on her lap. The old woman had quit this task at some point; no point trying to do needlework with a hawthorn barb when there's a bombardment on. Instead, she'd folded her grandmotherly hands, as if in prayer. The funeral was simple, as were most during the Petersburg siege. Even during funerals, after all, the Army of the Potomac continued shelling. Even during the hymn afterwards: *Amazing grace, how sweet the sound...*

But Ella Boisseau, sixteen years old and in fine voice, sang the song as if she never noticed the incoming artillery. She performed with the spry retainer Lewis over Athaliah's grave, and the harmony of her girl's soprano and his old man's bass sounded so liquid and gentle it was a if they had somehow managed to rise above the entire 250 years of Southern slavery.

But then, too, the girl was leaving. To the less magnanimous at the funeral, the ones too damaged by malnutrition and heartache to lose themselves in the beauty of Ella's singing, the only plausible explanation for how happily she sang had to be that she was getting out of Petersburg. While Grant's vast insatiable animal went on gnawing at the city's eastern defenses, Ella Boisseau—lucky girl!—was heading the other way. Albert and Andrew had arranged for her to stay with relatives in a road junction well to the west, far from the hostilities. She'd see out the duration in a crossroads called Five Forks.

It took hardly a day for Ella to get packed, hardly a half a day to have Lewis drive her out to the quiet crossroads. Yet it seemed to the teenager as if she'd gone to another world. The place was Burnt Quarter. A mansion before there even was a Union, it stood bright and welcoming, its tall chimneys towering over a roof that sprouted dormers, windows with green shutters, and a porch with white pillars. Its name was a mystery—perhaps named after a nearby creek—perhaps because the British had burned the slave quarters in an earlier war.

Greeting Ella on the portico were more of her family—the Gilliams—distant relatives, but people she could count on, nonetheless. "Come in, come in, Ella," beamed the warm-faced widow, Mary Gilliam. "I'm so sorry to hear about your grandmother. She was a fine lady."

Ella nodded, softly smiling, entering the house. Her eyes fell on her cousin, Albeena Gilliam, now twenty-three years old and in the full bloom of her womanhood. Ella herself was a pretty girl—people always told her so. But Albeena was more than pretty, she was a Southern beauty. Her wide brow was crowned with long curls that tumbled to her low-cut bodice. And her eyes. Ella loved to look into those blue eyes that were so beautiful, so kind.

The Widow Gilliam noticed Ella's admiring gaze. It was a look she had seen many times before. Her daughter had the reputation of being the most courted girl in the Confederacy. "If you observe a fair number of our Southern officers paying us a visit, well, you may understand why," the widow said proudly.

One of those visitors was a dashing young cavalry general, William Henry Fitzhugh Lee, a son of General Robert E. Lee himself. "Everyone calls him Rooney," Albeena told Ella. "The poor man's wife died last year, and he has no one else to talk to. He misses her very much—he is a very lonely man."

The man had other reasons for coming. Mary's other child, sixteen-year-old Samuel Yates Gilliam, knew the back roads in that area better than just about anyone, and he personally escorted the troops along the hidden routes.

Sometimes Ella would watch as the handsome young widower strolled through the garden daffodils with her lovely cousin. He in his gray uniform with gold-braided sleeves, his sabre at his side, and she in her hoop skirts, her bodice cut low. They seemed perfect together—almost too perfect. The brave man faced death day after day, and found refreshment to carry on in the sweet companionship of Albeena. Ella wondered if there would ever be so dashing a figure as Rooney Lee in her life. She wondered if she would have the warmth and support to offer a man when she became a woman, the way her cousin Albeena had.

Samuel Yates Gilliam was the same age as Ella. Lanky and sometimes awkward, he made Ella laugh when he seemed to trip over his own feet. But Ella admired his courage. When fighting erupted near Dinwiddie Court House, it was Sam, according to family legend (although no evidence exists), who led the Confederates to just the right place to surprise the Federals. He came home jubilant: "We whupped 'em!" he crowed. "Ol' Pickett chased Sheridan back to the Court House. We're goin' to run 'em all the way back North."

And in the glow of that moment, the family circle sharing in the Southern triumph and in Sam's part in it, Ella could almost believe that it might really happen. "Perhaps," she let herself dream in this small window of hope, "perhaps somehow it will all work out for the best."

The dream was shortlived, however. At the end of March, 1865, there came days of sheet-like rain through which beaten-down files of gray-clad infantrymen tramped like ghosts.

Ella clung to each spring day as if it might be the last. The peach trees behind the house were now in full bloom, their bright pink blossoms like clouds in a peaceful sunset. It was as perfect as the fine oil portraits that hung on the walls inside. The family was so kind, the house so lovely, the garden so peaceful. Ella's heart ached to hang on to this serenity, and to avoid forever the violence she had known back in Petersburg.

But for now, the peace she longed for existed only in her heart. The afternoon of April 1, Sam ran up the porch steps, flung open the door and dashed into the parlor. "It's happening," he said. "They're here."

The ladies rushed to the windows and saw gray-clad horsemen jumping the split-rail fence beyond the cornfield and thundering for the peach orchard behind the house. Moments later, the Bluecoats were right behind them, hordes of them, their horses knocking over the log rails as if they were nothing, the men shouting and charging into the cornfield.

In an instant, the shouts were drowned out by an ear-splitting fusillade of carbine shots from the Confederates in the peach orchard. The women held their ears and watched in horror as men and horses fell bleeding onto the grass. The shots rang back and forth between the two sides. One of the windows shattered—a bullet hole appearing on the wall behind.

One young Confederate sharpshooter was behind a big tree at the side of the mansion, picking off Yankees as they charged through the field. Albeena was watching from the parlor, and could see the boy was cut off from the rest of the troops. "He'll be killed if those Yankees ever get their hands on him," she said.

Albeena pushed wide the front door and yelled to him: "Come on! Run!" Through a hail of gunfire, the soldier—not much older than Sam—scampered across the grass, onto the porch, all the way through the house and out the back door to rejoin his unit. The Widow Gilliam was holding her heaving chest, while young Ella beamed at her courageous cousin.

By one o'clock the fighting had died down, each side withdrawing to regroup and get reinforcements. But the yard was littered with dead and dying soldiers and horses. The women and the slaves helped Union soldiers bring the wounded, blue and gray alike, into the dining room. They pushed the table and chair aside and laid a dozen bleeding men on the floor while a Union doctor tended them. Ella and Albeena washed wounds, brought tea and water, and spoke tenderly to the fallen.

The Widow Gilliam looked out the shattered window to see that the great clouds of black-powder smoke had wilted her peach blossoms as badly as a killer frost. "And look at this blood on the floor," she exclaimed. "It will take weeks to scrub it clean." She had had quite enough of this war, thank you. They could just take their foolish fighting somewhere else. Closing the doors to the dining room to keep out the groaning, she sat down and wrote a letter to Union commander Philip Sheridan. "You can move your battle," she wrote. "I cannot move my house." She put the letter in the hands of a trusted slave and sent him off.

She got her answer from her own side of the fight. Soon another slave arrived with a letter from the Confederates: a letter to Albeena from Rooney Lee. He thanked her for all the kindness she and her family had shown him, and apologized that he was unable to keep Sheridan's forces far from her farm. He felt she would be better off if she and the others left Burnt Quarter immediately, because the fighting she had seen that morning was a mere skirmish compared to the battle that was coming. He had taken the liberty to dispatch an ambulance to take her and her family to safety.

Albeena clutched the letter and allowed herself a quiet moment. She appreciated being cared about and protected by this Southern gentleman, but she hated to leave her home. When she told Ella they would have to flee, Ella smiled sadly. "I have been through this before and I know what you're feeling," she said. "Everything will work out fine—trust me."

The rout at Five Forks came on April 1—perhaps destiny's grim reminder that the joke was on the formerly comfortable South, given its foolish dependence on slavery. In the days that followed, while someone—vandals, soldiers, whoever—slashed the lovely portraits on the walls at Burnt Quarter, Ella learned that as soon as General Grant heard that his troops had overrun Five Forks, he marched straight into his tent and wrote out the orders for the final assault on Petersburg the next day. To her horror, she also learned that this last scene of pain and sorrow was played out where her family had spent so much happy time—at Tudor Hall.

The key assault had come before dawn on Sunday, April 2. In the darkness, the front-line shock troops had crept forward on their bellies. Most of the 4,000 last-ditch defenders at Tudor Hall were caught asleep. In the semi-darkness, the Yankees silently swept over the top of the earthworks, their banner floating against the gray sky. Then, their guns and their cheers erupted, destroying what remained of the night, and of the last defenses of the South. They captured Southern cannons, swung them around, and opened fire. In less than half an hour of chaos, they had torn their way to the South.

In the groaning weeks that followed, Ella Boisseau helped blue and gray alike, anyone who could make it to the hospital tents where she helped. And she heard many a Yankee infantryman, flat-voiced but victorious, call their Tudor Hall attack "the wedge that opened the home of the Confederacy."

CAPTURE OF THE WORKS AT PETERSBURG

The home, yes. Petersburg had finally been laid open to the Federals. The breakthrough came on back-to-back days, Saturday the First and Sunday the Second, and by some sudden startling flash of history's torchlight, each time on Boisseau property. The first was at Burnt Quarter, the second a few miles away—at Tudor Hall. It was as if once the Union had conquered this family, they'd won over the entire Old South.

Not that Ella understood all this on April Fool's Day. The best the courageous girl could do, that entire terrible weekend, was understand that she'd never suffered such close exposure, such a profound test of her new-forged compassion and goodwill. It was as if she'd inherited the eyes of her visionary grandmother Athaliah. She saw the kind of human devastation the old woman had told her about. And, as these last days of war wound down, she continued seeing to the wounded. Circulating tirelessly among the moaning, the dying, the teenager strove to recall every root and herb her Uncle Albert had taught her. She sent for old Lewis again, needing his memory, his advice. Together she and the old black man labored over the veterans of that final battle.

Together too, they heard of the war's end. The closing acts came, in another oddly fitting wrinkle of fate, during Christian Holy Week. The breakout at Tudor Hall was the first of a series of momentous events on succeeding Sundays. The next was April 9, Palm Sunday, when at Appomattox Court House Grant and Lee signed the documents ending hostilities. And the final awesome stroke came on April 16, Easter Sunday. That evening Ella was shocked to hear from a cavalry courier that Abraham Lincoln had died the day before, shot while attending a play, by a deranged actor. At a play, by an actor! It was like some cosmic reminder that this intrinsically American conflagration, so different from earlier European-influenced wars, was itself a drama played out in the palm of God's hand: a reminder that the Divine Mind had briefly but blisteringly focused on these few mid-Atlantic farmlands and hillsides—and on this family.

Through all the news good, bad, and inspiring, Ella and Lewis labored on. They concocted poultices, sleeping potions and fever reducers. To Ella there came to seem a special justice in their remedies. For how often had sick slaves, deprived of the white man's doctors, required the sort of woods medicine she and Lewis were brewing up these days? And now how much strange brew would her tragic new South need to drink in order to purge its system of its former disease?

Sometimes, as the pretty teenager and her seamy old friend circulated among the cots of the wounded, in the front rooms of the old plantation, the two of them would begin to sing again. Their twinned voices soothed the men around them. *Amazing grace*, Ella and Lewis sang, *how sweet the sound.* ... And as their voices rose, it seemed sometimes to patients and care givers alike as if they were all afloat in the air, some unimaginably peaceful summer air. Sometime the soldiers couldn't help joining in with rough harmony of their own: *that saved a wretch like me!* It was as if their linked voices were timeless, as if the yearning towards the hymn's salvation had been going on for centuries. The singing seemed to be climbing the air, climbing out of those fetid sickrooms, out of the human inferno altogether, as if its beauty were climbing the centuries.

PAMPLIN PARK CIVIL WAR SITE

THE HISTORY

At 4:40 a.m. April 2, 1865, a signal gun boomed from Union Fort Fisher, southwest of Petersburg. Moments later, waves of Federal soldiers swarmed across several hundred yards of broken, swampy ground toward elaborate Confederate fortifications defended by a brigade of North Carolinians.

The two sides clashed in a deadly hand-to-hand combat. Both armies lost heavily, but when the firing stopped American flags waved over a key portion of Robert E. Lee's previously impenetrable Petersburg perimeter. In less than 16 hours, the nine-month Siege of Petersburg would end. Appomattox was but a week away.

Today, the scene where these dramatic events unfolded is one of the country's finest privately owned Civil War battlefields. This battleground, known at the time as the Boisseau Plantation, contains some of the finest earthen entrenchments remaining from the Civil War.

When the land was threatened by timbering, the Association for the Preservation of Civil War Sites (APCWS) asked the Pamplin Foundation of Portland, Oregon, to help save the property. The Foundation purchased 103 acres and provided grants to the APCWS to develop and manage the historic site. Descended from the Boisseaus, the Pamplin family is dedicated to preserving the site of their ancestral home where so much Civil War history occurred.

THE BATTLES

It was mid-June 1864. As Union soldiers began digging in for a siege against Petersburg, Lt. Gen. Ulysses S. Grant plotted his strategy. He knew that the key to forcing Gen. Robert E. Lee to relinquish the city lay in severing its railroad supply lines. After Grant's initial assault against Petersburg failed, he decided to focus on the two major railroads that still remained open into the "Cockade City."

The Weldon Railroad ran south from the Confederate citadel, stretching into North Carolina and various points beyond. The South Side Railroad headed due west from Petersburg terminating in Lynchburg, Virginia. From there the South Side connected with other important rail lines racing deep into the heart of the Confederacy.

Almost immediately after ordering his men to build trench lines, Grant directed a force to capture the Weldon Railroad. The effort failed, but Union troops did gain ground closer to the railroad and across the Jerusalem Plank Road.

Again in mid-August following the disastrous Battle of the Crater, Grant once again aimed for the rail line. This time he captured the vital transportation link, gaining a foothold on the Weldon Railroad about six miles below Petersburg. A few days later, at Reams Station, fast-marching Confederate troops halted a Union effort to destroy the railroad even farther south.

Although Lee could no longer rely on an uninterrupted Weldon line to furnish his army, he devised a system that transported his supplies up the tracks as far as Stony Creek Station, eighteen miles south of Petersburg. The Southerners then placed their goods in wagons that rolled cross-country toward Dinwiddie Court House. Near this point they followed the Boydton Plank Road into the Confederate works. This route turned the old turnpike into an intermediate supply line of major significance.

In late September, Grant again placed his army in motion to strike the plank road and South Side Railroad beyond. Breaking through Confederate defenses along Squirrel Level Road at Peeble's Farm, the Federals pushed forward to another Rebel rampart built just south of the plank road (These are the trenches now in Pamplin Park). Here the Southerners held their ground.

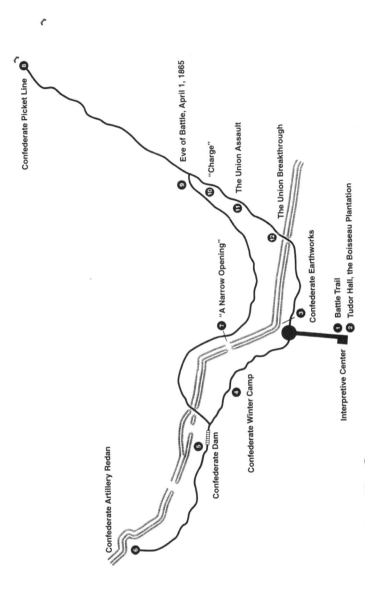

Confederate Picket Line

Eve of Battle, April 1, 1865

"Charge"

The Union Assault

The Union Breakthrough

"A Narrow Opening"

Confederate Earthworks

Battle Trail

Tudor Hall, the Boisseau Plantation

Confederate Artillery Redan

Confederate Dam

Confederate Winter Camp

Interpretive Center

PAMPLIN PARK CIVIL WAR SITE

The Federal army would make two additional but unsuccessful jabs at these goals during the next five months. The first would be at Burgess' Mill on October 27, 1864; the second at Hatcher's Run between February 5 and 7, 1865. (APCWS owns a portion of this battlefield, which you may visit.) Results of the later fight would allow Grant's forces to entrench even nearer to the plank road.

Meanwhile, the Confederates strengthened the defenses they built to protect the Boydton Plank Road. They also constructed their winter quarters directly behind the earthworks. In the area of Pamplin Park, Gen. Samuel McGowan's South Carolina brigade encamped while the general used the nearby Joseph Boisseau house, Tudor Hall, as his headquarters.

With the spring campaign imminent, Gen. Lee decided to launch an attack at some point east of Petersburg. He planned to draw Grant's forces from his western flank and the South Side Railroad by breaching Union positions to the east. The Battle of Fort Stedman on March 25 resulted from this strategy, and although initially successful, the Confederate attackers met overwhelming Union numbers and eventually retreated into their original lines. Taking advantage of the situation, the Federals assaulted Lee's picket line southwest of the city and captured a section of them near Forts Welch and Fisher. It would be from this advanced position that one week later the attack on the Confederate trenches in Pamplin Park would originate.

As Grant began his final offensive against Lee's supply lines on March 29, a series of engagements allowed him to maneuver his forces into position. In the late afternoon of April 1, Federal troops gained the extremely important crossroads known locally as Five Forks. Now the door lay open to capture the South Side Railroad.

Upon hearing the news of this achievement around 9 p.m., Grant strode into his headquarters tent and wrote a series of dispatches. Returning to his staff, he reported, "I have ordered a general assault along the lines (for tomorrow morning)."

The Union VI Corps, commanded by Gen. Horatio Wright, would lead the attack at a position he selected in advance. At around 4:40 a.m. on April 2 the initial assault would begin on a portion of the Confederate lines, about half of which survive today in Pamplin Park Civil War Site.

You can take a 1.1-mile walking trail to get further details of this critical engagement that cut Lee's army in half and eventually forced him to evacuate Petersburg.

APCWS

The Association for the Preservation of Civil War Sites was established to preserve historic Civil War battle sites. The goal of the APCWS is to secure, by donation, purchase, or legislative action, land on Civil War sites in all areas of the country that otherwise would be sacrificed to inappropriate development. This effort concentrates particularly on locations where sites face imminent destruction.

The APCWS seeks to acquire fee title to such land or secure permanent easements on it. The APCWS also supports local Civil War preservation efforts with technical assistance, interest-free loans, and cash grants, and works with Congress and state and local governments to enact legislation and acquire funding for Civil War battlefield preservation.

PAMPLIN PARK CIVIL WAR SITE
6523 Duncan Road
Petersburg, Virginia 23803
Phone: 804-861-2408
FAX: 804-861-2820
Open daily from 9 to 5
Memorial Day through Labor Day
Call for off-season hours.

PETERSBURG
AND THE OVERALL CAMPAIGN

PETERSBURG

The Pamplin Park Civil War Site is a part of the overall siege of
Petersburg. The Petersburg National Battlefield, now a part of
the National Park Service and the U.S. Department of the Inte-
rior, is nearby and contains 2,460 acres and is made up of six
major units.

THE OVERALL CAMPAIGN

The campaign that brought the armies to Petersburg and on to
Appomattox Court House began in May 1984 when the 122,000-
man Union army under Gen. Ulysses S. Grant crossed the Rapidan
River and engaged Gen. Robert E. Lee's Confederate army of 65,00
in a series of hard-fought battles. For a month the two armies
clashed, marched, and clashed again. After each encounter, Grant
moved farther southward and closer to Richmond. By the beginning of June, the Federals were within nine miles of the Confederate capital, but Lee still blocked their path. At Cold Harbor on
June 3, Grant tried by frontal attack to crush the Confederate army
and enter the city. He failed in a defeat marked by very heavy
casualties.

After Cold Harbor, Grant abandoned his plan to capture Richmond by direct assault. Instead, he moved his forces to the south
side of the James River and on June 15-18 threw them against
Petersburg, a key rail center on the Confederate supply line. The

city might have fallen then had Federal commanders pressed home their assaults and prevented the few Confederate defenders from holding on until Lee's army arrived from the north. When four days of combat failed to capture the city, Grant began siege operations.

THE COMMANDERS

Gen. Robert E. Lee commanded the Army of Northern Virginia, the main Confederate army in the East. His job was to defend Richmond-Petersburg front. When Union forces crossed the Rapidan and headed south in May, 1864, Lee told one of his officers, "We must destroy this Army of Grant's before he gets to the James River. If he gets there, it will become a siege and then it will be a mere question of time." Lee's worst fears were realized when the Federals reached the James River and beyond and settled down to besiege Petersburg. As the months passed and the Union army's grip on the city tightened, all Lee could do was try to stave off the inevitable as long as possible.

Lt. Gen. Ulysses S. Grant commanded all Federal forces as of March 1864 and possessed the authority to commit the total war resources of the Union against the Confederacy. His primary objective was to "get possession" of Lee's army. With the capture of [this] army," he said, "Richmond would necessarily follow." Grant's long campaign of attrition against Lee from the Wilderness through Spotsylvania and Cold Harbor to Petersburg has been called one of the first examples of modern warfare. Although taking an enormous toll in human lives, for which Grant was sharply criticized, it did help to wear down Confederate resistance and end the Civil War sooner than might have otherwise been possible.

THE BATTLES

In the grim 10-month struggle—the longest siege in American warfare—Grant's army gradually but relentlessly encircled Petersburg and cut Lee's supply lines from the south. For the Confederates it was 10 months of desperately hanging on, hoping the people of the North would tire of the war. For soldiers of both armies it was 10 months of rifle bullets, artillery, and mortar shells, relieved only by rear-area tedium; drill and more drill, salt pork and corn meal, burned beans and bad coffee.

Although Grant's first attempts to capture Petersburg from the east on June 15–18 failed miserably and cost him 10,000 men, his soldiers did manage to cut two of the railroads leading into the city and gain control of several roads. In August, he struck out to the south and west against the Weldon Railroad. After three days of fierce fighting in brutal heat, Union troops were astride the iron rails near Globe Tavern. Several days later, on August 25, Lee's Confederates scored a minor victory at Ream's Station, five miles south of Globe Tavern, but failed to break the Federal hold on the railroad.

By October, Grant had moved three miles west of the Weldon Railroad and the noose around Petersburg tightened. The approach of winter brought a general halt to activities. Still there was the everyday skirmishing, sniper fire, and mortar shelling. By early February 1865, Lee had only 60,000 cold and hungry soldiers in the trenches to oppose Grant's well-equipped force of 110,000. On February 5–7, Grant extended his lines westward to Hatcher's Run and forced Lee to lengthen his own thinly stretched defenses. Federal supplies rattled continuously over the newly completed U.S. Military Railroad from City Point to the front.

By mid-March, it was apparent to Lee that Grant's superior force would either get around the Confederate right flank or pierce the line somewhere along its 37-mile length. The Southern commander hoped to break the Union stranglehold on Petersburg by attacking Grant at Fort Stedman. Plans were to breach the Union line, hold the gap, and gain access to Grant's military railroad a short distance beyond. If it worked, Grant might have to relinquish positions to the west and Lee could shorten his own lines. On March 25, Confederates overpowered Fort Stedman only to be crushed by a Union counterattack.

With victory near, Grant unleashed Gen. Philip H. Sheridan at Five Forks on April 1. His objective: the Southside Railroad. Sheridan smashed the Confederate forces under George Pickett and gained access to the tracks beyond. On April 2, Grant ordered an all-out assault, and Lee's right flank crumbled. A Homeric defense at Confederate Fort Gregg saved Lee from possible street fighting in Petersburg. On the night of April 2, Lee evacuated Petersburg. Appomattox Court House, the site of the final surrender, was but a week away.

THE BATTLE OF THE CRATER

Shortly after the siege began, members of the 48th Pennsylvania Infantry, many of whom were coal miners before the war, began digging a tunnel toward a Confederate fort at Pegram's (sometimes called Elliott's) Salient, southeast of Petersburg. The plan: explode four tons of gunpowder under the salient and send a large body of troops through the gap created in the enemy's defenses by the explosion. If the plan succeeded, Petersburg might be captured without a long siege and the war could be shortened by many months.

The tunnel took a month to dig and was 511 feet long, with lateral galleries at the end to hold the powder. When the explosion took place on the morning of July 30, it blew up a Confederate artillery battery and left a crater about 170 feet long, 60 feet wide, and 30 feet deep. Union troops, instead of going around the crater, plunged directly into it and were unable to go any farther. Confederate counterattacks retook the position, inflicting around 4,000 Federal casualties. The siege would continue.

ABOUT THE AUTHORS

DR. ROBERT PAMPLIN has experienced incredible financial success. As an undergraduate in the 1960s he caught the rise of the stock market, making his first million. He later invested those profits in timber and farmlands, just before they shot up in value. And his $30,000 investment in an unproven "cutting" horse led to $2 million in stud fees, and the horse's eventual sale for $850,000.

His lifelong tutor has been his father. Together, they run a family company that owns 19 textile mills as well as a concrete and asphalt company. 1995 sales of the R.B. Pamplin Corporation were $800 million.

Dr. Pamplin has also authored ten books and earned eight degrees. He has served as chairman of both Lewis and Clark college and the University of Portland. He's been awarded many honorary degrees and has served on state and presidential commissions. *The Forbes 400* member resides near Portland, Oregon.

GARY K. EISLER is an award-winning writer whose work has appeared in *Forbes* and *The Wall Street Journal*.

JEFF SENGSTACK is a writer and video producer who recently concluded an 11-year career as an Emmy-winning television news reporter and anchorman.

JOHN DOMINI is coauthor of *The Encyclopedia Dictionary of English Usage and Bedlam*.

MASTERMEDIA LIMITED

To order additional copies of *Prelude to Surrender: The Pamplin Family and the Siege of Petersburg* send a check for $10.95 (please add $2 for the first book, $1 for each extra copy, for postage and handling), or *Heritage: The Making of an American Family* send a check for $24.95 for hardbound or $12.95 for paperbound (please add $2 for the first book, and $1 for each extra copy, for postage and handling) to:

MasterMedia Limited
17 East 89th Street
New York, NY 10128

(800) 334-8232
(212) 546-7638 (fax)

AN INVITATION

If you found this book helpful, you may want to receive an inspirational newsletter from **The Heritage Imprint**, a list of inspirational books from MasterMedia, the only company to combine publishing with a full-service speakers bureau.

MasterMedia books and speakers cover today's important issues from family values to health topics and business ethics.

For The Heritage Newsletter or a MasterMedia book catalog write or fax to the above address or phone number.

For information and a complete list of speakers, call (800) 453-2887 or fax (908) 359-1647.

NOV - 2010
(1999)